Contents

Oh, Tess!

Sam was taking Tess for a walk. Or, rather, he was trying to.

Tess was the dog next door. She was big and brown and bouncy and she loved to go for walks. Or, rather, she loved to run and jump and race. And, best of all, Tess loved to swim.

Sam had new shoes on. They were clean and white and still a bit hard, but Tess didn't care. She pulled Sam along the road and into the park, across the grass and through the mud. Sam had to run to keep up. His feet started to hurt.

"Slow down," he shouted. "Stop, Tess! Sit!"

But Tess took no notice at all. She just ran on and on until she got to the pond. Then she stopped and barked.

Sam sat down on the grass.

"My feet hurt," he said. "I'll have to take my shoes off."

Tess jumped up and down and barked again. Sam took off his shoes and put them down on the grass.

"What a silly dog you are," he laughed. "Come on. I'll get you something to play with."

Sam found a stick.

"Here, Tess," he shouted, and threw it up in the air. Splash! went the stick into the pond. Splash! went Tess as she jumped in and swam after it.

She was soon back with the stick in her mouth. She put it down at Sam's feet and barked again.

"Clever dog," said Sam.

Tess shook herself, splash! all over Sam.

"Oh no," said Sam. "Go away!" And he threw the stick into the pond again.

Sam threw the stick for Tess again and again until he got tired.

"Come on, Tess," he called. "It's time to go home now."

But Tess took no notice. She was in the pond and she wouldn't come.

"I'm not going to wait," said Sam. "I'll just get my shoes and go."

Sam went back to where he had left his shoes. He looked this way and that. He looked everywhere, but they had gone.

"Oh no!" he said. "Someone has taken my new shoes! What will Mum say!"

Tess barked. She was still in the pond.

"This is no time to play, you silly dog," said Sam.
"My shoes have gone, my new shoes. I've got to get help."

Tess took no notice. She just swam round and round
the pond. Suddenly she put her head down and dived
under the water. Then she came up again with an old
bottle in her mouth. She swam to the grass and put the
bottle down at Sam's feet.

"Stop playing about!" said Sam. "Come on now!"

But Tess wouldn't come. She jumped back into the pond, swam round and round and dived again. This time she came up with a big log in her mouth. Sam was getting cross now.

"Come here!" he said. "Come here at once!" But Tess took no notice. She just jumped in and dived again. Now Sam was very cross.

"You're a bad dog, Tess!" he shouted. "If it wasn't for you my feet wouldn't hurt. If it wasn't for you, my shoes wouldn't be lost. If it wasn't for you…"

Just then, Tess came up again. She held something in her mouth. What could it be?

Tess swam to the grass and dropped it at Sam's feet. Sam bent down and looked.

"My shoes!" he said. "You've found my shoes! You clever dog!" Tess barked and shook herself, splash! all over Sam again.

"Oh, Tess!" said Sam.

Cat burglar

Janey James can play the piano, and this is how she came to learn.

Mr Benson lived in the flat above Janey's. He was a music teacher and sometimes Janey could hear people playing the piano when she went past.

"Can I learn to play the piano, Mum?" asked Janey.

"We can't afford it," Mrs James told her. Janey would have liked to go into Mr Benson's flat and watch him playing, but Mr Benson never asked her in.

Janey's cat, Lucy, also liked the music, and she would sit outside Mr Benson's door.

"It's no good, Lucy," said Janey. "He won't ask us in."

But one day Mr Benson came to see Janey's mother.

"I'm going away for a week," he said. "Would you mind going up to my flat to water my plants while I'm away?"

"I'll be happy to," said Mrs James. Janey smiled. Now she would be able to see Mr Benson's piano.

So while Mr Benson was away, Mrs James went to water his plants, and Janey went with her. The piano was in the living room and Janey tried to play it.

"Don't do that," said Mrs James. "We are here to water Mr Benson's plants, not to play his piano."

"Where is Lucy?" said Janey, when they were outside the flat.

"I thought she was with you," said Mrs James.

"She must still be in there," said Janey. They looked all over the flat, but they couldn't find Lucy.

"She must be in the garden," said Mrs James. "Never mind. Lucy will come back later."

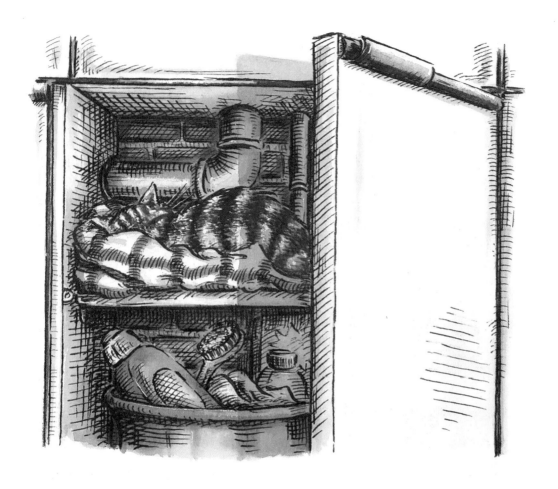

But Lucy **was** in the flat. She had got into a cupboard with a warm water pipe at the back. She curled up, and soon she was asleep.

The time went by. At last, Lucy woke up. She came out of the cupboard and went to the door of the flat, but it was shut. So Lucy went and found a big chair and curled up in that.

Janey was worried when Lucy didn't come home. When she went to bed, she couldn't sleep. She was too worried about Lucy. She was still not asleep when Mrs James went to bed.

"Has Lucy come home?" asked Janey.

"No," said Mrs James. "Don't look so worried, Janey. Lucy can always get through the cat flap. Now, go to sleep."

But Janey couldn't sleep. She waited to hear the noise of the cat flap to tell her that Lucy had come home.

Janey wasn't the only one who wasn't sleeping.
There was also a burglar who was getting into
Mr Benson's flat! He had watched the flat and guessed
that the man who lived there was away. He climbed up
the tree to the window and broke in.

The burglar turned on his torch. He was in a
bedroom. There was a television on a small table next to
the bed.

"I'll have that," he said, with a smile.

But just then, he heard something!

"Music!" he cried. "Who's making that noise? There's no one else here! This place must have ghosts!" He dropped his torch and it broke and went out. Then there was more music.

"Help!" shouted the burglar, and he ran into the next room. He fell over something, hit his head on a table and knocked himself out.

Janey sat up in bed. She was sure she had heard a noise. What was it? Music?

"It's coming from Mr Benson's flat!" she cried. "Mum!"

Before they went up to Mr Benson's flat, Janey's mum did the right thing. She telephoned the police.

When the police came, they soon found out who was making music. It was Lucy!

"Oh dear," Mrs James said to the policeman. "We called you out for nothing."

The policeman was looking behind one of Mr Benson's big chairs.

"No, you didn't," he said. He looked at Janey and smiled. "I think you and your cat have helped to catch a burglar."

When Mr Benson came back, Janey's mum told him about Lucy and the burglar.

"She made a terrible noise," said Janey.

Mr Benson laughed. "Perhaps Lucy should learn to play the piano!"

"It's Janey who wants to learn to play the piano," said Mrs James.

"Is it, now?" said Mr Benson. "Well then, I had better be her teacher."

"But we can't afford –" began Mum.

"Never mind that," said Mr Benson.

And that's how Janey came to learn to play the piano.

Pickle Monster Mucky Scruff

There once was a kitten who had no family and no name.

"Have you got a name yet?" the other kittens would ask him when they met in the street.

"No, no name yet," the kitten would say, sadly.

"You must find a family," the other kittens would tell him. "A family will give you a name."

The kitten came to a garden where a woman was cutting the grass. The kitten saw that there were children's clothes on the washing line.

"Good," he thought. "There must be children in the house, and children like kittens."

"Pickle Monster," Mum called to Jessie.

"I wish you wouldn't call me that," said Jessie. "It makes me feel silly."

"Sorry," said Mum. "I just wanted you to see this kitten."

"It's just a baby!" cried Jessie, and she picked up the kitten and stroked it. "You funny little thing. You're the one who's getting into a pickle," she said. "You should be called Pickle Monster, not me."

David came into the garden.

"Hello, Mucky Scruff," said Mum. "Come and look at this."

David looked cross.

"Don't call me that," he said. "It's a silly name and it makes my friends laugh at me." He went over to have a look at the kitten.

"Let me hold it," he said to Jessie.

"Only while I get it some milk," she said. "Because it's my kitten. I saw it first."

"It's mine as much as yours," said David. "It's my house too." And he stroked the kitten and said,

"You poor, muddy little thing. You should be called Mucky Scruff, not me."

The kitten played with Jessie and David all day.

"Can I keep him?" asked Jessie. "His name is Pickle Monster, and he's just what I've always wanted."

"Can I keep him?" asked David. "I'll look after him. And his name is Mucky Scruff."

"I'll think about it," said Mum.

The kitten heard all this and was very worried.

"Have I got a family or not?" he thought. "And if I have, which of those is my name?"

Later, they took the kitten into the house and gave it some milk and a box to sleep in. Then Mum said,

"All right. I've made up my mind about the kitten. You can keep him, if he wants to stay here, but only if you share him."

"Great!" said Jessie. "We'll call him Pickle Monster."

"Oh no we won't," said David. "His name is Mucky Scruff."

"Well," said Mum, "let's see which name he answers to."

The kitten listened to all this from his box.

"Oh dear," he thought. "I don't know which one is my real name!" He was frightened that he would answer to the wrong one.

"Pickle Monster," called Jessie. "Come to me, Pickle Monster, there's a good kitty." But the kitten was too frightened to come out of his box.

"Mucky Scruff," called David. "Come to me, Mucky Scruff." But the kitten didn't know what to do.

Mum looked at the children,

"Pickle Monster, Mucky Scruff," she said. "This won't get us anywhere."

That sounded like the best name of all, so the kitten suddenly jumped out of his box and ran up to them.

"Pickle Monster Mucky Scruff," they all laughed.

The kitten sat at their feet and purred. This was his own name and his own family, and he was happy at last.

Pets

My teacher said at the end of term
We could bring our pets to school.
Jane brought her frog. Ted brought his dog.
Dave Barry brought his mule.
I brought my pet Diplodocus
Who sleeps beside my bed.
He snores and whistles all night long
Through a small hole in his head.
My teacher came to pat our pets
And said that they were nice.
Though when she got to Diplo
I could see her thinking twice.

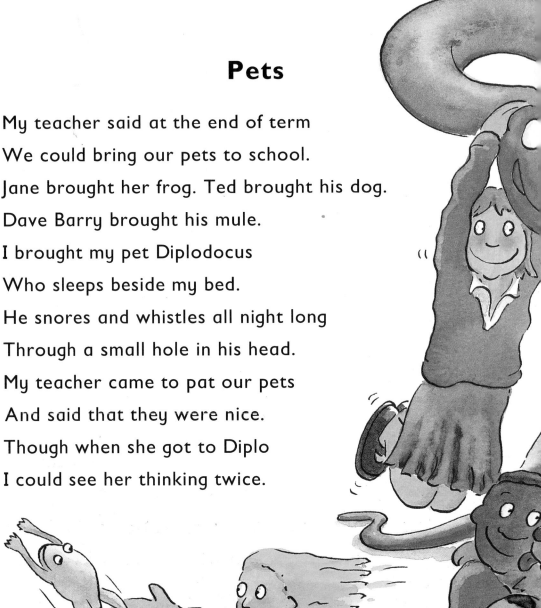

But Diplo smiled his widest smile
And let her stroke his head.
But, "I'm very pleased to EAT you"
Was **not** what he should have said.
My teacher fainted clean away
And fell and bumped her head.
Now when it comes to end of term
We've to bring a book instead.

Margaret Ryan

Kim at school

When Chris and Debbie got to school one day, they had a surprise.

"Hello," said Susie. "Who's your new friend?"

"What new friend?" asked Debbie. She turned round to see. There was Chris and Debbie's dog, Kim.

"Kim! You bad dog!" said Debbie. "Go home now!" But Kim had gone to play with Chris and Ali.

"Chris! Make Kim go home!" shouted Debbie. Just then the school bell went.

"We've got to go in now," Chris said to Kim. "You go home."

Kim didn't want to go home. She ran into the school before the children could catch her and went and hid behind some books. Soon, some children came to look at the books.

Suddenly, Kim saw Chris so she jumped out. She wanted to play. Bang! went the books!

"You bad dog!" shouted Chris. "Go home!" So Kim ran away but she didn't go home.

She ran along and went to find Debbie. At last she saw her. She was painting a picture. The picture looked good to eat! Kim ran in and tried to eat the picture. Oh! It was not good to eat!

Kim jumped up and tried to get away. Splash! went the water, all over Kim and all over the table and all over Debbie's painting.

"You bad dog!" shouted Debbie. "Go home!"
Kim didn't go. She just shook the water off her fur. When everyone was very wet, she ran away again.

Next she found some children running and playing.
It looked fun. Kim watched for a second and then she
went in and tried to play too. She barked and jumped
about and ran round the room. All the children laughed
and shouted. They helped the teacher to try to catch her.

"Watch out!" shouted Mr Jones, but Kim was running
so fast that she couldn't stop. Bump! went Kim. Oh!
Kim didn't like that at all, so she jumped up and ran away.

She ran out of the room and out of the school and along the street, all the way home. She sat down on the path and licked her bump. Then she went to sleep in the sun to let her fur dry.

When Chris and Debbie came home from school, Kim's bump had gone and she was clean and dry.

"You made lots of trouble at school today," said Chris.

"I hope you'll never try to come to school again!" said Debbie. And Kim never did.